793.7
MOS

Mosler, Gerard

The puzzle school

DATE DUE

THE
PUZZLE
SCHOOL

THE
PUZZLE
SCHOOL

Gerard Mosler

Illustrated by
Frank C. Smith

Abelard-Schuman
New York

Library of Congress Cataloging in Publication Data
Mosler, Gerard.
  The puzzle school.
  SUMMARY: Includes a variety of puzzles arranged by
school subjects such as mathematics, science, fine arts,
social studies, and language arts.
  1. Puzzles—Juv. lit. [1. Puzzles]
I. Smith, Frank Charles, 1937–   II. Title.
GV1493.M625 1977   793.7'3   75-45428
ISBN 0-200-00168-X
10 9 8 7 6 5 4 3 2 1

CONTENTS

PUZZLES

SOLUTIONS

PUZZLES

MATHEMATICS

1. STRETCH THAT COFFEE!

You have a cup of coffee before you of which you drink one-sixth. Then you pour as much milk into the cup as you drank of coffee. You drink one-third from this mixture and pour again as much milk into the cup as you drank of the mixture. Now you drink one-half of the cup; then, for the last time, you fill it up with milk again and drink the whole cup.

Can you tell whether you had more milk or more coffee and how much of each?

2. POCKET MONEY ON CONDITION

A father, hard pressed by his son for an extra dollar, gave it to him on one condition: Sonny must bring home 100 pieces of candy that cost 10 cents, 3 cents and ½ cent each, respectively. Sonny met the condition.

Can you tell how many pieces of candy of each kind he brought home?

3. HOW GOOD A CUBIST ARE YOU?

The 18 cubes shown here have different design patterns on some of them. Your task is to find three "families" of 6 cubes each—each of which belongs to the same design pattern. In order to complete this test successfully, you must observe well and think logically at the same time.

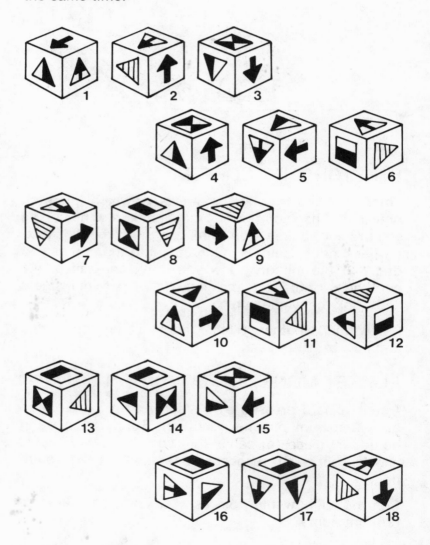

4. THE MEASURE MESS

Each of the people listed from 1 to 11 can be associated with just one of the specific measures listed from a to k. Example: 1. Jeweler would match with e) CARAT, carat being the unit of weight for gold and jewels. Make 8 or more correct matches for a weighty score.

1. Jeweler	7. Bricklayer	a) Cord	g) Scruple
2. Surveyor	8. Horse	b) Hand	h) Furlong
3. Stationer	trader	c) Perch	i) Caliber
4. Farmer	9. Apothecary	d) Fathom	j) Chain
5. Gunmaker	10. Jockey	e) Carat	k) Ream
6. Mariner	11. Lumber-	f) Bushel	
	man		

5. BOAT-MEETING

Every day at noon, a ship leaves Le Havre, France, for New York. At the same time, a ship of the same company leaves New York for Le Havre. The crossing of each ship takes exactly seven days. Now—how many "fellow ships" will the ship leaving Le Havre today meet on its way to New York?

6. BUYING HEADS BY THE FOOT

Somebody bought as many spears of asparagus as could fit into the circle made from a foot-long string. The next day, the same person brought a string two feet long and bought as much asparagus as this string would encircle. When he offered the grocer twice as much money as on the preceding day, can you tell whether the grocer . . .

a) got very angry?
b) accepted it as a matter of fact?
c) thanked him for his generosity?

7. BE A FIGURE TRACER!

Can you deduce, logically, which number should be in the small circle containing the question mark?

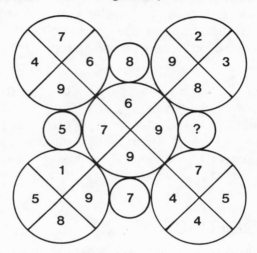

8. HOW WHEEL-RIGHT ARE YOU?

By turning the handle in the direction indicated by the arrow, can you tell whether the cover of the box will go up or down?

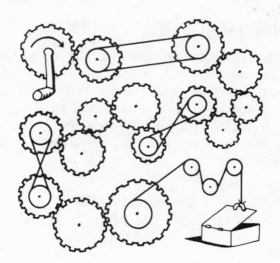

9. HIT THE JACKPOT—BUT HOW?

There is going to be a big prize hidden in one of the pots to be awarded to the competitor who hits the correct pot with the stick. On the eve of the competition a super-smartie tries to examine the pots through the show window but the organizers of the contest, in wise anticipation, have secreted the pot with the prize.

By examining first the pots at bottom and then comparing them with the ones shown at the competition, can you deduce which of the ten pots above must have been the one containing the prize?

10. STRIKING FIGURES FOR '76

```
7  7  7  7  7
7  7  7  7  7
8  8  8  8  8
8  8  8  8  8
9  9  9  9  9
9  9  9  9  9
```

Can you strike out two squares and leave the numbers that add up to this country's fateful number of '76?

11. HOW LONG IS AN "AGE"?

The actual length of an "age" cannot specifically be determined. However, there are some words for very definite periods of time listed here in the left column. Try to match these with the exact time spans shown at right. A score of 8 and over is very timely.

1. Decade
2. Millennium
3. Eon
4. Quarantine
5. Sennight
6. Semester
7. Lustrum
8. Generation
9. Ephemeral
10. Indiction
11. Biennium

a) Forty days
b) One week
c) Two years
d) One half year
e) One thousand years
f) Eternity
g) Fifteen years
h) Thirty years
i) Ten years
j) Five years
k) One day

12. A VERY WEIGHTY PROBLEM

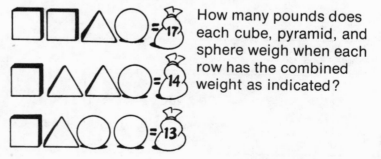

How many pounds does each cube, pyramid, and sphere weigh when each row has the combined weight as indicated?

13. HOW ODD?

If any number of coins is placed on a table by other people (the exact number being unknown to you), you can give any odds that you will be able to add coins to the pile so that if the number is an even one you will make it into an odd number, or if it is an odd number you will make it into an even one.

Do you know, though, what you would have to do?

14. ILLUMINATION, PLEASE!

On both sides of a street, there are 45 lanterns, each one at a distance of 30 yards from the other. The lamps on one side are so arranged that each lamp here fills out the gap between two others on the other side.

How long is the street?

15. STARRY CHAIN REACTION

A former movie star staying at a fashionable hotel, but temporarily out of cash, told the manager she was expecting a large amount of money in 11 days. In order to show her goodwill for making daily payments, she promised to turn over to the management one link of her gold belt (picture below) for a day's rent. This is the problem. She wants to give the hotel a link a day and, because she expects to redeem the belt after 11 days are up, she does not want to cut up the belt any more than necessary.

What is the minimum number of cuts required?

16. A DRIVER'S PROGRESSIVE PROBLEM

An automobilist starts a week's vacation on Monday and finishes it the following Sunday by driving twice as many miles each day as on each preceding day.

Can you tell how many miles the automobilist would drive on Friday when he covered 381 miles in all?

17. HOW CLOCK-WISE ARE YOU?

Each of these clocks, whose mirror images you see here, strikes the hours, and all clocks are running fine. Can you tell which clock will strike the hour first, and how many strikes it will make?

18. V-EXAMINATION!

Can you make this multiplication come out correctly by substituting figures for the letters?

$$\frac{\begin{array}{r} \text{VEXATION} \\ \times \qquad \text{V} \end{array}}{\text{EEEEEEEE}}$$

19. ARE YOU A GOOD RAILROAD ENGINEER?

Here is an intriguing problem that will keep you busy for a while: There are eight locomotives placed on this strange, circular railroad track arrangement. Your task now is to shunt the locomotives, one by one, along the tracks, moving either forward or backward. Use as few moves as possible. A move is the shunting of one locomotive from one letter to another. To start you off, move locomotive 7 from A to B. In the end the eight locomotives should be placed in correct numerical order (1, 2, 3, 4, 5, 6, 7, 8) around the circular track. Please note that one locomotive is damaged and cannot move at all.

(We suggest that you cut out small paper disks, number them from 1 to 8, and use these for handy "shunting" on the diagram.)

Can you do the job in less than 20 moves?

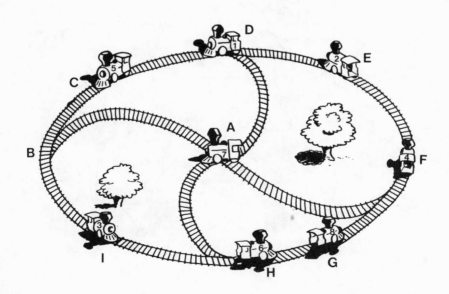

20. THE SHOW IS SLIPPING

Half the students slipped out of a boring lecture in the first 15 minutes; a third of the rest in the next 15 minutes; and a quarter of the remainder in the next 15 minutes, leaving only nine students to cope with the dope.

How many students had there been at the beginning?

LANGUAGE ARTS

1. LET'S PLAY TYPEWRITER!

How many words can you trace out of the alphabet above, which represents the letter arrangement on all typewriters? You may start at any letter and move from left to right, or upward, or downward, but *never from right to left.* You may skip as many letters as you wish. Example: You may spell out the word SERF without skipping; or the word EVIL by skipping from E to V to I all the way to L. All words must have four or more letters. Try to reach—or even beat—our score of 40 words. A score of 30 and over is very good, though.

2. DO YOU KNOW A PRIMER FROM A PAMPHLET?

Words in the left column designate specific types of books or printed documents. Can you match each of these with the identity of each type of book given in the right column? A score of 9 or more correct matches is a "prime" score.

1. Pamphlet	a) An extended treatise on some subject
2. Primer	b) A register for visitors' names
3. Encyclopedia	c) Contains words of an opera
4. Tome	d) A handbook for quick reference
5. Album	e) A collection of literary selections
6. Dissertation	f) An elementary reader
7. Opus	g) Plots and incidents of a motion picture
8. Manual	h) Usually has a paper cover
9. Lexicon	i) A literary or musical work
10. Anthology	j) Information on all subjects
11. Libretto	k) A large book
12. Scenario	l) Alphabetic arrangement of word definitions

3. HOW WELL CAN YOU WIELD THE BLUE PENCIL?

Most people speak more than is necessary for their own good as well as for that of good speech. Now then—can you improve each of the following sentences by deleting just one word?

A real editor you if you can spot 15 or more of the superfluous words!

1. Will you repeat the message back to me?
2. I tracked down the rumor to its original source.

3. The higher dignitaries preceded before all others in the procession.
4. I cut the apple into two halves.
5. A repeat performance will be given on Wednesday morning at 11 A.M.
6. The company charged with setting up an exclusive monopoly denied the accusation bitterly.
7. Is your helping adequate enough?
8. The doctor's prognosis for the future development of this case was good.
9. The addressee is the person to whom the letter is addressed to.
10. I think I have a grasp of the important essentials.
11. The house has recently been newly renovated.
12. These two girls look like twins in almost every respect.
13. It is suggested that we start first by standing up in memory of our late colleague.
14. The man fell down from the third-story window.
15. The superintendent asked the handyman to sweep the cellar off.
16. That seems to be the universal opinion of the gathering in this room.
17. The isolated patient had to be under quarantine for at least two more days.
18. When the speaker was asked for a better explanation he merely reiterated what he had said before.
19. The present incumbent does not take his official duties too seriously.
20. You are quite all right if you have scored 15 or more in this test.

4. TRANSFORMATION, PLEASE!

By changing one letter in each of the words, you can transform this into a well-known proverb.

COME IN THERE SHE HEARD IT.

5. PICTORIAL WORD-BUILDING

The words for each of the pictures shown here can be combined to form new words. Example: FLY+ WHEEL=FLYWHEEL. Don't give up too soon. There are quite a few more words than you might suspect at first.

A super word-builder you if you can come near our score of 20 or even beat it.

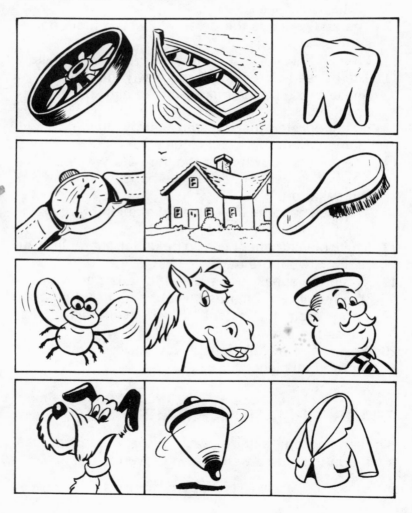

6.   "OOH!"—AND THIS IS A CLUE!

Each word defined below rhymes with all the other words—YET all words have different endings! Get 10 or more for a good score!

1. Hint
2. Boat
3. Animal
4. Couple
5. Indian

6. Food
7. One
8. Tryst
9. Antelope
10. Ruminate

11. During
12. Grass
13. Nonsense!
14. Beginning
15. Place

7.   WHERE DOES SHE HIDE?

If you and I take her out from where she is hiding, we will be left all alone; but when you and you are taken from where you two are, she will still be in here.

Do you know what all this double-talk is about?

8.   "AS"SIMILATION, PLEASE!

Each of the pictures shown here should bring to mind a well-known assimilative phrase. For instance: white AS snow, yellow AS gold would be such assimilative phrases. Find ten or more such phrases and you'll have a score as good AS any language expert would have.

9. "TERMINASHUN," PLEASE!

A dozen words—phonetically—end in SHUN, although no two spellings of the endings are alike. How many of these words can you spell correctly by substituting for the phonetic sound SHUN the endings as they are spelled correctly? A score of 10 or more is shun-sashunal!

1. MENSHUN
2. COERSHUN
3. RUSHUN
4. ASHUN
5. VENESHUN
6. GRESHUN
7. MANSHUN
8. FASHUN
9. LUNSHUN
10. STANSHUN
11. PASHUN
12. OSHUN

10. PROVERBIAL PROVIDENCE

The proverbs listed here were set up by a thrifty printer who decided to be economical with his type. Whenever a letter in the original proverb was repeated he ignored it, i.e. the letters were put in the first time but not the subsequent times. Example: O U T F S I G H M N D would be OUT OF SIGHT OUT OF MIND. Can you be as provident as our printer by reconstructing the original proverbs? A score of 10 and over is very good!

1. H O M E I S W R T A
2. A M I S G O D L E
3. F O R W A N E D I S M
4. O N E M A S T I H R P
5. A S T I C H N M E V
6. S O M A N Y E I D
7. O N E S W A L D T M K U R
8. F O R G I V E N S B T H A
9. A F R I E N D S
10. T W O F A R D E N V G
11. A L I S N O T G D H E R
12. N E C S I T Y K O W S L A

13. O N E C A T P L S H W R D I F
14. T W O W R N G S D M A K E I H
15. E V R Y O S M U T H A V I N
16. A L T H E W O R D V S
17. E X P R I N C S T H B A
18. I F A T R S Y O U D N C E Y G

11.   CAN YOU TEACH ENGLISH TO A FOREIGNER?

The following story may well serve as an example of the simplicity as well as the intricacy of the English language.
Simplicity because the Frenchman in the story was well understood despite the incorrect use of an important word. Intricacy? Well, see for yourself whether you can find the most appropriate word in each instance where the length of each word is indicated by dashes. A score of 15 or over is very good.

A Frenchman while looking at a number of vessels exclaimed: "See, what a flock of ships!" He was told that a flock of ships was called a fleet but that a "fleet" of sheep was called a (1) _ _ _ _ _ _. To assist him in mastering the intricacies of the English language he was further told that a flock of girls is called a (2) _ _ _ _ and a flock of wolves is called a (3) _ _ _ _, though a flock of thieves is called a (4) _ _ _ _ and a flock of angels is called a (5) _ _ _ _, while a flock of oxen is called a (6) _ _ _ _ and a flock of porpoises is called a (7) _ _ _ _ _. He was instructed that a flock of bees is termed a (8) _ _ _ _, while a flock of locusts is called a (9) _ _ _ _ _ and a flock of puppies is known as a (10) _ _ _ _ _ _ and a flock of young birds is called a (11) _ _ _ _ _. They told him further that a flock of children is called a (12) _ _ _ _ _, and a flock of partridges is termed a (13) _ _ _ _ _ _, while a flock of beauties is known as a (14) _ _ _ _ _ _, although a flock of barbarians is called a (15) _ _ _ _ _ and a flock of rubbish is a (16) _ _ _ _.

To his utter bewilderment, they further told him that a flock of bullocks is called a (17) _ _ _ _ _, whereas a flock of gangsters is known as a (18) _ _ _ and a flock of whales is known as a (19) _ _ _ _ _ _ and a flock of worshipers a (20) _ _ _ _ _ _ _ _ _ _ _ _ _ and, finally, a flock of engineers a "corps." The last word, being French, the Frenchman understood perfectly and asked no more. What about you?

12. CANADIAN BABEL

The inhabitants of a Canadian town speak either French or English or both. Seventy-three percent speak French and eighty-seven percent speak English. What percentage speaks both languages?

13. INTERNATIONAL PERSONNEL KNOWLEDGE

If you were a personnel manager, which of the two applications—to be decided on the applicant's strength in foreign languages—would you take into further consideration: the one claiming knowledge of German, Dutch, Czech, and Urdu, or the other also claiming German and Dutch, in addition to Brazilian, Greek, and Chinese?

SCIENCE

1. HOW LAVISH IS NATURE?

If you don't know the answers to the following questions, some of which you may have asked yourself before, just make your best possible guess from the choice of three answers given. Score 9 or more correct guesses and you are the nearest thing to a "natural phenomenon" yourself.

HOW MANY . . .

1. . . . stars can you see (with the naked eye) from any one place on earth?
   - a) 7,500
   - b) 27,000
   - c) 270,000

2. . . . molecules (smallest amount of matter) would have room on the dot of this "i"?
   - a) 1 Million
   - b) 1 Trillion
   - c) 1 Quintillion

3. . . . quarts of blood are pumped
by your heart through the blood
vessels in one day?

a)   120
b)   1,200
c) 12,000

4. . . . tons of ashes did the eruption of the volcano Krakatau
produce in 1883?

a) 18 million
b) 18 billion
c) 18 trillion

5. . . . pounds of dust go into the
lungs of an average city dweller
during an average lifetime?

a)   4½
b)   45
c) 450

6. . . . times more powerful is the
shock of even a slight earthquake than the blast of an atom
bomb?

a)   10
b)   100
c) 1,000

7. . . . different insects are living
with us on this earth?

a) 700,000
b) 500,000
c) 100,000

8. . . . pounds of meteors fall
upon the earth in one year?

a)   20,000
b)   200,000
c) 2,000,000

9. . . . eggs are there in the
average sturgeon?

a)   30,000
b)   300,000
c) 3,000,000

10. . . . red blood cells are contained in a tiny drop of blood
about this size: "•" (1 cubic millimeter)?

a)   500,000
b)   5,000,000
c) 50,000,000

11. . . . tons of dissolved minerals
are swept into the Atlantic by the
Mississippi every second?

a)   ½
b)   4
c) 40

12. . . . pounds of gold are contained in each cubic mile of the
Pacific?

a)   4
b)   400
c) 40,000

2. THE PROBLEM OF THE CHANGING LAB SCENE

The two illustrations differ in at least 20 instances. To be rated a good observer, find 16 or more.

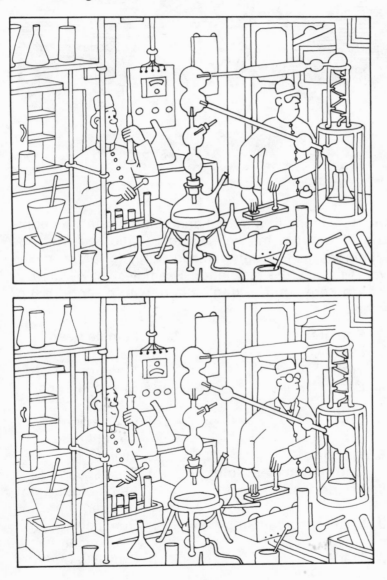

3. TWO-FACED FREAKS

The definitions in the left-hand column refer to people who differ from the animals to be guessed from the definitions in the right-hand column (given in mixed order) in only the first letter. Example: 1e: *Wizard/Lizard*. You are "outfreaking" nature with a score of 8 or better.

1. Sorcerer	a) Female deer
2. Enemy	b) Eel
3. Tutor	c) Alligator
4. Desert dweller	d) Shaggy-haired beast
5. Chef	e) Four-legged reptile
6. Prophet	f) Insect
7. One who makes cloth	g) Crustacean
8. Nonprofessional man	h) Amphibious rodent
9. Shakespearean king	i) Ruminant mammal
10. Trader	j) Crowlike bird

4. SINK OR SWIM?

Everybody knows that trees don't sink when thrown into water. An iron nail, however, would sink immediately. Yet there are metals that float and woods that sink—depending on whether their specific gravity is greater or less than that of water. Can you tell which of the items listed here come through the trial by water and SWIM (float) and which SINK? Score swimmingly with 12 or more correct guesses.

1. Leather
2. Ebony
3. Glycerine
4. Oak
5. Milk

6. Dry plaster
7. Alcohol
8. Ice
9. Ivory
10. Celluloid

11. Beer
12. Rubber
13. Champagne
14. Aluminum
15. Charcoal

5. THE PROBLEMATIC HEN PARTY

Hen #2 is heavier than Hen #1; Hen #4 weighs more than Hen #5 but less than Hen #3; Hen #5 weighs more than Hen #1. Finally, Hen #3 weighs less than Hen #2. Knowing now everything about the respective weights of the hens, can you list them in the order of their weights, starting with the heaviest?

6.   HOW GOOD A WEATHERMAN ARE YOU?

Sometimes we are under the weather and sometimes we are not. But we are always with the weather, or rather the weather is always with us. There is hardly a person who does not have his or her own notions about what the weather does to people. Here is a test that may knock out many a popular belief about the weather and reinforce some truths in others.

Get 15 or more of the answers right, by answering yes or no, and you have weathered this test splendidly.

1. The best behaved children in the world can be found in cold or temperate zones rather than in the warm ones.
2. "Rain before seven, clear before eleven!"
3. More babies are conceived in the summer than in any other season.
4. Changes of weather conditions can be felt in old scars and fractures.
5. Natives of mild southern climates have a greater resistance to infectious diseases than those in cold climates.
6. When dogs eat grass, it is going to rain.
7. The so-called Trade Winds blow from northeast to southwest in the Northern Hemisphere.
8. Vacationers should welcome nimbus clouds and beware of cumulus clouds.

9. A falling barometer makes us more inclined to be cross and irritable than an unchanging barometer.
10. Between June 1 and July 15 the North Pole receives more heat than an equal area anywhere on earth.
11. Lightning does strike twice in the same area.
12. Coffee and similar slight stimulants are less damaging in the tropical zones than in temperate zones.
13. People in the tropics have a greater tolerance for alcohol than people in cold zones.
14. The death rate is highest at temperatures over 75 degrees Fahrenheit.
15. A hard winter is due when muskrats have heavy pelts and squirrels lay up an unusually large store of nuts.
16. The funnel cloud of a tornado moves from southwest to northeast.
17. Heavy battles will bring on a storm.

18. A rainbow in the morning is the shepherd's warning!
19. It is possible to estimate how far away a flash of lightning is.
20. People are more apt to be overcome by heat on a moist day than on a very dry day.
21. Sea breezes during the daytime are caused by land warming up more quickly than water.

22. When swallows fly high, the weather is going to remain nice; when they fly low to the ground, a weather change may be expected.
23. Sound travels faster in summer than in winter.
24. Winters are not as cold anymore as in grandfather's time.
25. People who are especially tense during a thunderstorm are just victims of their imagination.

7. ANIMAL DOUBLE-TALK

The names of animals of all kinds also mean something entirely different in our language. Guess the words from the definitions below and these words will then be the same as for an animal representative of the respective groups below. For example, a pugilist is a boxer (5 letters), and a boxer is a breed of dog. A score of 25 or more is very good.

DOG WORDS

1. Pugilist (5 letters)
2. Useful hint (7)
3. Food; victuals (4)
4. Chinese citizen (8)
5. Rough in tone; harsh (5)
6. Clay mixed with water (3)
7. Compositor (6)
8. Large island (12)

BIRD WORDS

1. Assistant (8 letters)
2. Church official (8)
3. Chess piece (4)
4. Flags (collectively) (7)
5. Merriment (4)
6. Asiatic country (6)
7. Hoisting device (5)
8. Long pole (5)

HORSE WORDS

1. Small glass (4 letters)
2. Compartment (3)
3. High hill (5)
4. Egyptian (4)
5. Revolver (4)
6. Gemstone (4)
7. Cutting instrument (7)
8. Goblin (4)

FISH WORDS

1. Deep sound (4 letters)
2. Accidental luck (5)
3. Elevated seat (5)
4. Hilltop (4)
5. Metal runner (5)
6. Stiff collar (5)
7. Beam (3)
8. Part of a shoe (4)

8. DO YOU KNOW THE TIMES OF THEIR LIVES?

The average life span of one animal in each of the ten pairs shown here is just about 10 years longer than that of the other. Check the animal which—in your estimation—has the longer life of the two in each pair. A good life insurance agent you if you get a score of 8 or more.

WHO	OUTLIVES	WHOM?
1. Whale		Elephant
2. Antelope		Horse
3. Gorilla		Dog
4. Moose		Leopard
5. Giraffe		Hippopotamus
6. Coyote		Camel
7. Buffalo		Porpoise
8. Lion		Fox
9. Cat		Bear
10. Cow		Tiger

9. FALLACIOUS, ISN'T IT?

The snapshots here of a tree were taken from the same angle but at different times. Can you reestablish the chronological order of the ten pictures?

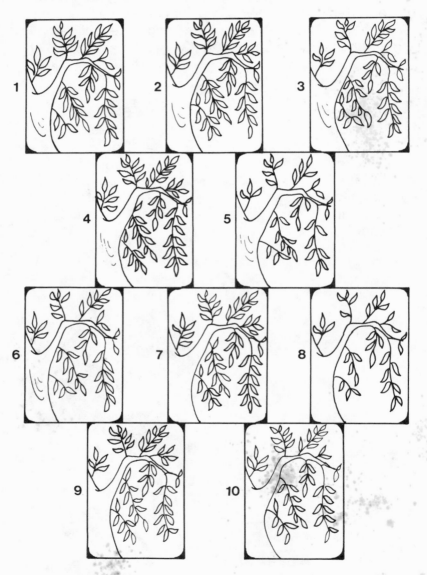

10. DON'T LET THESE TREES STUMP YOU!

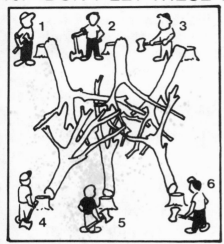

The problem here is to judge a tree fellers' contest. Can you tell which of the woodsmen felled his tree in the shortest time, and who are the runners-up and in which order?

11. SOUND TRACK AT THE ZOO

The English language excels in particularization. When a dog makes a noise, he BARKS, HOWLS, YELPS or GROWLS. These are the particular words applied to canine sound. Here's a list of 24 animals. The idea is for you to give the word which is used to describe how each of these creatures sounds off. There may be more than one word applicable to certain animals, and more than one animal that can be associated with a particular sound.

A score of 18 or more of them correctly identified is very sound.

1. Cats	9. Lions	17. Pigs
2. Hogs	10. Pheasants	18. Stags
3. Bulls	11. Cows	19. Sheep
4. Ducks	12. Wolves	20. Crows
5. Snakes	13. Donkeys	21. Geese
6. Hens	14. Frogs	22. Goats
7. Elephants	15. Bees	23. Beetles
8. Mice	16. Monkeys	24. Owls

12. COLORFUL NONSENSE

Now this is all nonsense BUT if snow were red, grass were black, the sky brown, blood white and soot green—well, what color would your cup of coffee turn out to be according to the new color scheme?

13. CONSERVATION, PLEASE!

Can you tell how one can keep beef fresh for several years without a freezer?

14. DAMN THE MOSQUITOES!

In one of the few scarcely explored spots in South America the mosquitoes are so numerous that a good many of them weigh a pound. They are also very ferocious. They sit on the logs and bark when explorers go by. Can this be true?

15. KNOW YOUR ENEMY

Insects do millions of dollars worth of damage to our crops every year, but most of us are more concerned with how furiously annoying they can be. This true-or-false test should give you some surprising facts about the bugs and the bees. And it should also help you protect yourself from them.

1. Mosquitoes don't bite; they "stab."
2. Millipedes, centipedes, ticks, mites and spiders are not insects.
3. Flies live only a few days.
4. A bee dies immediately after it stings you.
5. Silent mosquitoes do not attack; only the ones that hum do.
6. Mosquitoes are attracted by light, not darkness.
7. Fireflies shine as much during the day as at night.
8. Insects do not have skeletons, brains, hearts, blood or glands.
9. Insects cannot easily survive a severe winter.
10. The tropics have more insects than the temperate zones.
11. Houseflies are annoying, but don't do much harm.
12. There are no insects in the Arctic Zone.
13. Insects never sleep.
14. Insects can live on after their heads are cut off.
15. In sum, the majority of insects are harmful to man.

FINE ARTS

1. WHOSE PRICELESS THOUGHTS?

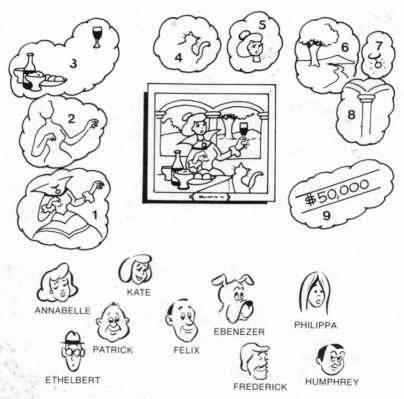

Here is a priceless painting of a nice girl, critically judged by eight people and a dog—each of whom has his or her "thoughts" about the picture—"thoughts" grouped pictorially around the painting. Match each person with his or her "thought" and then take the first letter of the person's name thinking thought #1 and the second letter of the second person's name thinking thought #2 and so on to the ninth thought and the ninth letter in a name. These nine letters will spell out what each of these people thinks to be.

2. CAN YOU SET THE QUARTET?

The names of four players in a quartet are Arthur, Bert, Clare and David. They are playing the violin, the piano, flute and cello. They meet in Arthur's apartment. The cellist, a bachelor, has an hour's ride before he gets home after the performance. Clare and David met for the first time at a concert and have been married for five years. The violinist once gave a Beethoven biography to David for his birthday, while David and Clare put their respective instruments on each other's Christmas table last Christmas. Can you tell from the above information which of the four persons is playing which instrument?

3. DOUBLE ARTISTRY IN A SPLIT SECOND?

Test your observation by telling in a moment whether the model weight lifter fits into the frame or not.

4. OH, SWEET MYSTERY OF MODERN ART!

Taking the ten people listed at right as his subject matter, our "smalltime Picasso" has come up with the pictures shown here. Most ARTful you if you see through six or more correct matches.

a) Lawyer f) Porter
b) Bar fly g) Writer
c) Athlete h) Glutton
d) Robber i) Poet
e) Don Juan j) Tramp

5. ADDLED ARTISTS IN THE GOOFY GALLERY

If you were visiting the goofy gallery in which the addled artists were displaying their masterpieces, how many mistakes could you find in, let's say, two minutes.

6. HOW POP "ART"FUL ARE YOU?

Can you tell which of the patterns occupies the most space in the design shown here: the black, the white, the dotted, the crisscross, the bricklike one or the striped one?

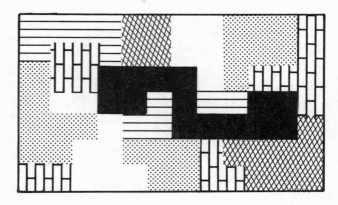

7. MORE POP "ART"FULNESS

A simple answer to a simple question here: how many curved lines were used within this figure?

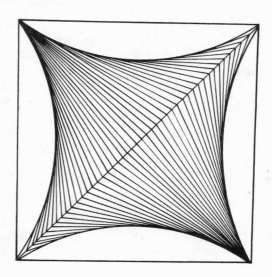

8. SCOTTIES, SCOTTIES EVERYWHERE

A master of silhouettes, obviously in love with his Scotty, has produced this picture in black and white. Can you puzzle out how many Scotties, black, white, or black and white, can be seen here?

SOCIAL STUDIES

GEOGRAPHY

1. METROPOLITAN LANDMARKS

Here are famous landmarks of the world's great cities. Can you name the city brought to mind by each picture? Get a good (land)mark with a score of 8 or more.

2. WATCH YOUR STEP!

If you take one step to the right, it's Sunday; if you take one step to the left, it's Monday; one step forward, and you will come into summer, and one step backward, and you will come into winter.

Do you know where you are?

3. WATCH THAT STATE LINE!

If a peacock belonging to an Iowa farmer would run away and lay an egg on a railway track in Minnesota, would the egg belong to the farmer, the state of Minnesota or the railroad company? This is a problem every layman should be able to decide.

4. COUNTRIES, ISLANDS AND TOWNS— WITHOUT CAPITALS THEY'RE NOUNS!

Many geographical localities become just words meaning a great many things when they are written as ordinary nouns, i.e. with a lower-case first letter. The TURKEY may serve as an example. If spelled *Turkey,* it is, of course, the country we are thinking about, and if spelled *turkey,* it's the bird we have in mind. Similarly, we have listed here the definitions of such words which—when spelled with a capital letter—emerge as a country, an island or a city. Get 20 or more correct answers for a really "capital" score in Geography.

WHICH WORD WHEN CAPITALIZED MEANS . . .

A COUNTRY OR ISLAND?

1. A large bird (Asia)
2. A hand-plaited hat (C.A.)
3. Goatskin leather (Afr.)
4. Red dyewood (S.A.)
5. Singing birds (Afr.)
6. Unbleached linen (Eur.)
7. A seasoning (S.A.)
8. Porcelain ware (Asia)
9. Former English gold coin (Afr.)
10. A liqueur from orange peels (S.A.)
11. Hard black varnish (Asia)
12. An evergreen tree (Eur.)

A CITY?

13. A sacred, fabled bird (Ariz.)
14. A round dance (Mass.)
15. A large sausage (Italy)
16. A kind of pepper (S.A.)
17. A fine cotton fabric (India)
18. A hard variety of quartz (Mich.)
19. Colored glazed earthenware (Netherlands)
20. A bonnet or fowl (Italy)
21. An evening dress coat (N.Y.)
22. A citrus fruit (N.J.)
23. The body of a vessel (England)
24. A humorous poem of 5 lines (Ireland)

5. ARE YOU AN INTERNATIONAL CLOTHES-SLEUTH?

Your task here is to identify the nationality of the person wearing a costume particular to his or her country and then match these persons with the respective anagrams given below in mixed order. Example: Match #8 with e) and get "Greek." A super clothes-sleuth you if you get eight or more correct matches.

a) Drain sap
b) I O U bend
c) UNs airs
d) Ruin Ghana
e) Re keg
f) Match cons
g) In camera
h) In a din
i) Apes Jane
j) Red on hall
k) Ant bite

6.   TALL TALES FROM THE SOUTH

Here is a report from one of the participants in a recent expedition to the South Pole: ". . . When we left the Pole we had to brave a terrific southwest wind. Only with great efforts could we make our way in a westerly direction. We were very tired as we had slept only the few hours between sunset and sunrise. . . ."

How many inconsistencies can you find in the above excerpt?

7.   . . . AND A PUZZLING SNAPSHOT
FROM MEXICO

Only two of these Mexicans are alike in all respects. Can you tell which two?

8. WHERE TO FIND A REPRESENTATIVE ABROAD

In the left column we have listed the names for the legislatures of a score of foreign countries which are shown in the right column in mixed order. Can you match both columns? A score of 15 and over is excellent.

1. Diet		a)	Russia
2. National Assembly		b)	New Zealand
3. Yuan		c)	Finland
4. Rigsdag		d)	Argentina
5. The Chambers		e)	England
6. States General		f)	Denmark
7. Supreme Soviet		g)	Switzerland
8. Storting		h)	Israel
9. Cortes		i)	Turkey
10. Riksdag		j)	Portugal
11. Grand Assembly		k)	China
12. Parliament		l)	France
13. National Congress		m)	West Germany
14. Bundestag		n)	Holland
15. Oireachtes		o)	Japan
16. Bundesrat		p)	Spain
17. Cortes Geraes		q)	Sweden
18. Knesset		r)	Ireland
19. General Assembly		s)	Norway
20. Eduskunta		t)	Belgium

HISTORY

1. WHO SAID WHAT IN AMERICA?

Each of the famous phrases can be attributed to just one famous American listed somewhere in the right column. You'll be doing historically well if you can match ten or more of the celebrities with their utterances.

1. "A house divided against itself cannot stand."
2. "The business of America is business."
3. "Prosperity is just around the corner."
4. "What hath God wrought?"
5. "The world must be made safe for democracy."
6. "Speak softly and carry a big stick."
7. "The Nation which indulges towards another an habitual hatred or an habitual fondness is in some degree a slave."

a) Franklin Roosevelt

b) John Wilkes Booth

c) Abraham Lincoln

d) Woodrow Wilson

e) General Israel Putnam

f) Patrick Henry

g) William J. Bryan

8. "Nuts!"

h) Samuel Morse

9. "Is life so dear or peace so sweet as to be purchased at the price of chains and slavery?"

i) Calvin Coolidge

10. "Quarantine the disturbers of world peace."

j) Brig. Gen. McAuliffe

11. "You shall not crucify mankind on a cross of gold."

k) George Washington

12. "Men, aim low and don't fire until you see the whites of their eyes."

l) Stephen Decatur

13. "Sic semper tyrannis."

14. "You may fire when you are ready, Gridley."

m) Theodore Roosevelt

15. "Our country! In her intercourse with foreign nations may she always be in the right; but our country, right or wrong!"

n) Herbert Hoover

o) Admiral Dewey

2. PRESIDENTIAL WORD FORMULA

This may be a stab at your credulity but there is really only one of our first 38 presidents whose name can be successfully anagrammed into just one other ordinary word.

What president? What word?

3.   HOW "SHIPSHAPE" ARE YOU?

Some ships gained fame through the people who sailed on them while others made a reputation for themselves by themselves. Can you identify, from the descriptions below, the names of the famous ships to which they refer? Historically "shipshape" you if you can dredge up a score of 7 or more.

WHAT SHIP . . .

1. . . . owned by Captain John Glover officially ranks as the "Mother of the Navy"?

WAS SAILED BY . . .

2. . . . Columbus when he discovered America?
3. . . . the Pilgrims when they landed at Plymouth Rock?
4. . . . Captain William Bligh who was later set adrift by rebellious sailors?
5. . . . Admiral Halsey into Tokyo Bay and became the scene of Japan's formal surrender?
6. . . . Napoleon when he was exiled to St. Helena?

SANK WHEN . . .

7. . . . it collided with an iceberg in the North Atlantic in April 1912?
8. . . . it was blown up in Havana harbor in February 1898?
9. . . . it (being American and neutral) was torpedoed by German submarines off Ireland in 1915?
10. . . . its own German crew blew it up off Montevideo in 1939?
11. . . . Union forces scuttled it at Portsmouth, Virginia?
12. . . . it foundered in heavy seas off Cape Hatteras in 1862?

4.   CONSTITUTIONAL CHESTNUTS

Why is a vote in Congress like a bad cold? . . . and
. . . what is the difference between Congress and
progress?

5.   THE MIXED-UP MIDDLE AGES

This illustration represents a "contemporary" snapshot
from a street scene in the Middle Ages. Unhappily, the
artist has been somewhat sloppy and a number of mistakes have crept into the picture. Look for items that
could not possibly have been in existence at that time.
A sharp observer of history you if you can detect 15 or
more items that do not belong.

6. WHO WAS "I"?

Each of these famous men made one of the statements listed in the right column. How many of these famous men can you match with their statements? A score of 9 and over is very good.

1. Abraham Lincoln
2. Julius Caesar
3. Edward VIII
4. Nathan Hale
5. Calvin Coolidge
6. Winston Churchill
7. Benjamin Franklin
8. Louis XIV
9. Patrick Henry
10. Franklin Roosevelt
11. Henry Clay
12. Theodore Roosevelt

a) "I have nothing to offer but blood, toil, tears, and sweat."
b) "I do not choose to run."
c) "I am as strong as a bull moose."
d) "I came, I saw, I conquered."
e) "I believe this government cannot endure permanently half slave and half free."
f) "I now quit altogether public affairs, and I lay down my burden."
g) "I only regret that I have but one life to lose for my country."
h) "I would dedicate this nation to the policy of the good neighbor."
i) "I would rather be right than be President."
j) "I know not what course others may take, but as for me, give me liberty or give me death!"
k) "I am the state."
l) "I shall never ask, never refuse, never resign an office."

7. PIECEMEAL PEACE MEAL

Two Indian scouts brought their sketched observations of a peaceful Indian settlement back to their home base. Can you tell in how many details the two sketches vary from one another? A score of 12 or more is very good.

8. WHO'S IN WHOM?

Each of the famous personalities below contains the name of another famous personality whose thumbnail biography you will find somewhere at the bottom of the page. Example: EISEN*HOWE*R contains the name of e) HOWE, inventor of the sewing machine. How many famous personalities within famous personalities can you identify by correctly matching both groups? A score of 15 and over is matchless!

1. EISENHOWER	11. SCHUMANN
2. OFFENBACH	12. SCHOPENHAUER
3. HAMILTON	13. GOETHALS
4. SULLIVAN	14. NOSTRADAMUS
5. MENDELSSOHN	15. ABELARD
6. HOPKINSON	16. LONGFELLOW
7. VOLTAIRE	17. SWEDENBORG
8. BRYANT	18. DISRAELI
9. STRAUSS	19. BELLAMY
10. RALEIGH	20. LINDBERGH

a) First man

b) Second son

c) Inventor of telephone

d) Dutch painter

e) Inventor of sewing machine

f) Movie Scarlett O'Hara

g) Movie and TV comedian

h) Foremost German novelist

i) Former prime minister

j) Russian czar

k) Discoverer of the laws of heredity

l) American surgeon introducing anesthesia

m) Hebrew patriarch

n) English poet of *Paradise Lost*

o) American educator

p) Statesman, lecturer, secretary of state

q) Swedish singer

r) Italian physicist, pioneer in electricity

s) German musician, composer, organist

t) Austrian composer of operettas

9.   WORDS IN INDEPENDENCE DAY

Start at any letter you wish, and proceed to any adjoin-
ing letters, horizontally, diagonally or vertically, and
spell out as many four- or more-than-four-letter words
as you can. Example: Start at the E in the upper left
corner, go from there to P, and then E and another E
for the word EPEE, one of the 20 words we have been
able to find. Can you reach—or even beat—our score?

E	N	D	E
P	E	C	N
E	D	A	Y
D			
N			
I			

HOME ECONOMICS

1.   ADD THE "INGREDIENTS" AND EAT YOUR MENU!

If you add one letter at a time contained in the word
INGREDIENTS to each of the "word dishes" on the
"menu" below and then rearrange the letters of each
word, you will get a complete real menu as a result. Example: The answer to number 1 is SARDINE by adding
one E from the word INGREDIENTS. All the letters of
the word INGREDIENTS should be used up in the end.
A good menu spotter you if you get nine or more
dishes correctly.

1. DRAINS

2. VIOLS   3. NOONS

4. THROBCS

5. BASE   6. OVINES   7. VARY

8. SPRAY

9. BAITERS

10. DANCES   11. SEAT

2. CAN YOU SPOT THE TWIN COOKS?

Only two of the chefs shown here in action are alike in all respects. Can you find them in a "twin"kling?

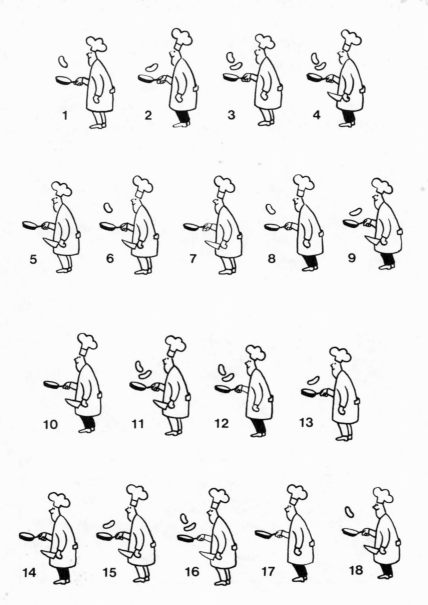

3. POT AND PITCHER LOGIC

Study the first two rows of items of chinaware carefully. Then turn to the third and fourth rows. The third row is incomplete, and it is your job to pick the one item of the choice of seven in the fourth row which would logically complete the third row.

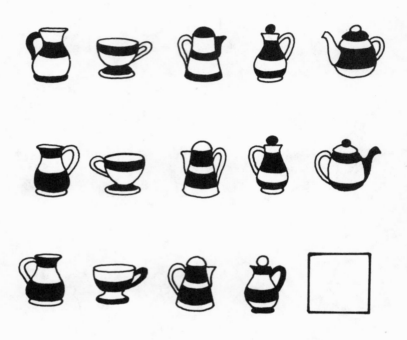

4. TO EACH HIS OWN—CAKE!

Your task here is to think of a kind of cake which you would appropriately give to each of the people listed below. In order to lead you on, we may tell you in the way of an example that DATE cake would be just the right thing for a CALENDAR MAKER. The number of dashes corresponds to the number of letters in the names of the cakes to be guessed with one letter already inscribed by us. Top the cake with a score of 8 or over!

WHAT CAKE WOULD YOU GIVE TO A . . .

1.	Calendar maker?	_ _ T _
2.	Milliner?	_ _ _ _ O _
3.	Geologist?	_ _ _ E _
4.	Sculptor?	_ A _ _ _ _
5.	Grocer?	_ _ _ C _
6.	Dairyman?	_ H _ _ _ _
7.	Weatherman?	_ _ _ _ H _ _ _
8.	Emperor?	_ _ _ _ _ I _ _
9.	Midget?	S _ _ _ _ _
10.	Idler?	_ O _ _
11.	Bridegroom?	W _ _ _ _ _ _
12.	Boxer?	R _ _ _ _

5. ARE YOU A KITCHEN DETECTIVE?

You and your family go into a restaurant and all of you order hot soup with dumplings in it. When the soup is served, mother begins to complain that the soup has not been freshly cooked but has only been heated up. You are doubtful, but when you begin to eat the steaming soup, you have to admit that mother is right. Why?

6. "EGG"OCENTRIC HOUSEWIFE

A housewife hard pressed to divulge the secret of her excellent cake at last consents to giving the following cryptic information: "It's all a matter of eggs." When asked: "But how many eggs?" she says: "If I had used three times as many eggs as I did use, I would have used as many over a dozen as I have really used under a dozen." Can you tell how many eggs she did use in her cake?

7. HOUSEHOLD TRUTHS OR MYTHS?

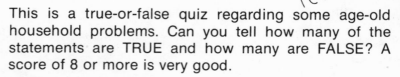

This is a true-or-false quiz regarding some age-old household problems. Can you tell how many of the statements are TRUE and how many are FALSE? A score of 8 or more is very good.

1. Moths eat clothes.
2. The sun shining into a room raises the dust.
3. Only smelly odors are dangerous.
4. A soft-boiled egg that has been allowed to get cold can be boiled hard by reboiling.
5. Skimmed milk is not nutritious.
6. Standing water is usually bad to drink.
7. Wine kept in bottles becomes stronger with age.
8. Brown eggs are not as nutritious as white eggs.
9. Drinking hot tea in warm weather cools the person who drinks it.
10. A thin glass can stand hot water better than a thick one.
11. Clothes are better dried in high wind than in sunshine.
12. The thawing process causes pipes to burst.

8. ON HEAD OR FOOT?

All you have to do here is to say whether the words listed below refer to headgear (H) or footgear (F), and you have done well with a score of 15 or over.

1. Tarboosh
2. Fedora
3. Wellington
4. Boston
5. Deerstalker
6. Blucher
7. Buskin
8. Busby
9. Balmoral
10. Biretta
11. Petasos
12. Oxford
13. Hessian
14. Gibus
15. Capuchin
16. Stogy
17. Chopine
18. Beaver
19. Billycock
20. Brogue

9. PICK YOUR PATTERN!

Can you tell which of the seven patterns has been chosen for the little girl's dress?

10. PICK UP THE PIECES!

Can you tell how many dishes fell victim to the clumsiness of the unfortunate carrier?

11. EAT YOUR WORD TOTALS!

If you guess the correct words from the definitions below you will get the word for something edible as a result. Example: number 1 is PUMP/KIN. How many "edible word totals" can you find in this way? A score of 9 or more is very good.

1. Water-raising device PLUS relative
2. Prohibition PLUS collection
3. Fourteenth letter PLUS plunge
4. Hand covering PLUS at home
5. Husband PLUS proceed
6. Daddy PLUS dog's foot
7. Mongrel dog PLUS noisy talk
8. Owned PLUS wharf
9. Stylish PLUS knowledge
10. Vessel PLUS monkey
11. Brisk energy PLUS through
12. Thus PLUS above
13. Gash PLUS permit

12. BOTTLE IMPERFECTION

Two bottles of the array of 19 bottles at left have some-how not been quite perfectly made, and their broken pieces now lie on the floor. Can you spot the two im-perfect bottles?

SOLUTIONS

MATHEMATICS

1. STRETCH THAT COFFEE!

As much milk as coffee: One-sixth and one-third and one-half make exactly one cup. That's the amount poured into the cup, and the amount of coffee that had been there originally.

2. POCKET MONEY ON CONDITION

$$
\begin{array}{llll}
5 \text{ pieces at } 10¢ & \text{equals} & 50¢ \\
1 \text{ piece at } 3¢ & \text{equals} & 3¢ \\
\underline{94 \text{ pieces at } \frac{1}{2}¢} & \text{equals} & \underline{47¢} \\
100 \text{ pieces} & & \$1.00
\end{array}
$$

3. HOW GOOD A CUBIST ARE YOU?

2-3-5-9-11-14
4-6-8-10-16-18
1-7-12-13-15-17

4. THE MEASURE MESS

1e, 2j, 3k, 4f, 5i, 6d, 7c, 8b, 9g, 10h, 11a.

5. BOAT MEETING

15 ships: When the first boat leaves Le Havre, it meets the boat that left New York exactly a week before. From there on, it will meet *two* ships every day for a total of 15.

6. BUYING HEADS BY THE FOOT

a: A circle double of another in circumference is also double in diameter. The area, however, of such a circle grows *four* times in size.

7. BE A FIGURE TRACER!

9: All numbers in one line horizontally and vertically add up to 30.

8. HOW WHEEL-RIGHT ARE YOU?

Up.

9. HIT THE JACKPOT—BUT HOW?

Pots 1, 3 and 7 have their handles intact, as do three of the pots in the show window. Pots 4 and 8 can be identified through the show window. This leaves pots 2, 5, 6, 9 and 10 as possibilities for holding the jackpot. The lengths and shapes of the handles of pots 2, 5, 6 and 10 can be seen repeated on the remaining pots in the show window, which leaves pot *9* as the one containing the jackpot.

10. STRIKING FIGURES FOR '76

Strike out upper-right square (consisting of four 7s) and lower-left square (consisting of eight 8s and eight 9s), which leaves:

Six × "7" equals 42
Two × "8" equals 16
Two × "9" equals 18

———
76

11. HOW LONG IS AN "AGE"?

1i, 2e, 3f, 4a, 5b, 6d, 7j, 8h, 9k, 10g, 11c.

12. A VERY WEIGHTY PROBLEM

Cube: 6 pounds; pyramid: 3 pounds; sphere: 2 pounds.

13.   HOW ODD?

Just add one coin!

14.   ILLUMINATION, PLEASE!

660 yards: There are 23 lamps on one side and 22 on
the other. There are 22 gaps between 23 lamps, therefore the street is 22 times 30 yards long, or 660 yards.

15.   STARRY CHAIN REACTION

Only one cut is necessary: Cutting the fourth link from
the left will divide the belt into two chains of 6 and 3
links each and two single links. She may now give one
link the first day, another single link the second day, a
three-link chain in exchange for the two single links on
the third day. This process continues on for 11 days.

16.   A DRIVER'S PROGRESSIVE PROBLEM

48 miles: Monday, 3 miles; Tuesday, 6 miles; Wednesday, 12 miles; Thursday, 24 miles; Friday, 48 miles; Sat-
urday, 96 miles; Sunday, 192 miles.

17.   HOW CLOCK-WISE ARE YOU?

Clock 4 will be the first to strike the hour, *five* o'clock,
in 6 minutes. The other clocks will strike their hours as
follows:

Clock 5 will strike the   3rd hour in 16 minutes
Clock 8 will strike the   6th hour in 20 minutes
Clock 3 will strike the   3rd hour in 25 minutes
Clock 1 will strike the 12th hour in 30 minutes
Clock 2 will strike the 10th hour in 31 minutes
Clock 7 will strike the 10th hour in 35 minutes
Clock 6 will strike the 2nd hour in 40 minutes

18. V-EXAMINATION!

```
98765432
       9
─────────
888888888
```

19. ARE YOU A GOOD RAILROAD ENGINEER?

The shunting can be done in 17 moves:

```
 1. Move engine 7 from A to B
 2.    "        "   6   "    H  "  A
 3.    "        "   3   "    I  "  H
 4.    "        "   7   "    B  "  I
 5.    "        "   6   "    A  "  B
 6.    "        "   1   "    D  "  A
 7.    "        "   2   "    E  "  D
 8.    "        "   4   "    F  "  E
 9.    "        "   1   "    A  "  F
10.    "        "   3   "    H  "  A
11.    "        "   8   "    G  "  H
12.    "        "   1   "    F  "  G
13.    "        "   3   "    A  "  F
14.    "        "   2   "    D  "  A
15.    "        "   4   "    E  "  D
16.    "        "   3   "    F  "  E
17.    "        "   2   "    A  "  F
```

20. THE SHOW IS SLIPPING

36 students.

LANGUAGE ARTS

1. LET'S PLAY TYPEWRITER!

1. Quip	14. Agio	27. Drip
2. Whip	15. Aery	28. Drop
3. Whop	16. Arty	29. Drum
4. Ergo	17. Serum	30. Gulp
5. Echo	18. Setup	31. Hump
6. Etui	19. Ship	32. Zebu
7. Ethiop	20. Shop	33. Crop
8. Rump	21. Scum	34. Crump
9. Ecru	22. Stop	35. Chip
10. Awed	23. Sect	36. Chop
11. Awful	24. Scrip	37. Chum
12. Axil	25. Scup	38. Chump
13. Awry	26. Snip	39. Viol
		40. Bump

2. DO YOU KNOW A PRIMER FROM A PAMPHLET?

1h, 2f, 3j, 4k, 5b, 6a, 7i, 8d, 9l, 10e, 11c, 12g.

3. HOW WELL CAN YOU WIELD THE BLUE PENCIL?

1. back; 2. original; 3. before; 4. two; 5. A.M.; 6. exclusive; 7. adequate or enough; 8. future; 9. to; 10. important; 11. newly; 12. two; 13. first; 14. down; 15. off; 16. universal; 17. isolated; 18. before; 19. present; 20. quite.

4. TRANSFORMATION, PLEASE!

Home is where the heart is.

5. PICTORIAL WORD-BUILDING

1. Dogwatch	11. Wheelhouse
2. Watchdog	12. Topcoat
3. Boathouse	13. Brushman
4. Housetop	14. Watchman
5. Housecoat	15. Topman
6. Doghouse	16. Boatman
7. Dogtooth	17. Houseman
8. Housefly	18. Toothbrush
9. Horsefly	19. Horseman
10. Houseboat	20. Wheelman

6. "OOH!"—AND THIS IS A CLUE!

1. clue; 2. canoe; 3. ewe; 4. two; 5. Sioux; 6. ragout; 7. you; 8. rendezvous; 9. gnu; 10. chew; 11. through; 12. bamboo; 13. pooh; 14. debut; 15. lieu.

7. WHERE DOES SHE HIDE?

The word "where": which becomes "we" without "her" and "here" with "w" (two "u").

8. "AS"SIMILATION, PLEASE!

1. Pale as a ghost	7. Tough as nails
2. Fresh as a daisy	8. Sober as a judge
3. Neat as a pin	9. Clear as crystal
4. Tired as a dog	10. Light as a feather
5. Sharp as a razor	11. Pretty as a picture
6. Red as a cherry	12. Fat as a pig

9. "TERMINASHUN," PLEASE!

1. men tion; 2. coer cion; 3. Ru ssian; 4. a shen; 5. Ve-ne tian; 6. Gre cian; 7. man sion; 8. fa shion; 9. lun cheon; 10. stan chion; 11. pa ssion; 12. o cean.

10. PROVERBIAL PROVIDENCE

1. Home is where the heart is.
2. A miss is as good as a mile.
3. Forewarned is forearmed.
4. One man's meat is another man's poison.
5. A stitch in time saves nine.
6. So many men, so many minds.
7. One swallow does not make a summer.
8. Forgiveness is better than revenge.
9. A friend in need is a friend indeed.
10. Two of a trade never agree.
11. All is not gold that glitters.
12. Necessity knows no law.
13. One cannot please all the world and his wife.
14. Two wrongs do not make a right.
15. Every rose must have its thorn.
16. All the world loves a lover.
17. Experience is the best teacher.
18. If at first you don't succeed, try, try again.

11. CAN YOU TEACH ENGLISH TO A FOREIGNER?

1. flock; 2. bevy; 3. pack; 4. gang; 5. band; 6. herd; 7. shoal; 8. hive; 9. swarm; 10. litter; 11. brood; 12. troop; 13. covey; 14, galaxy; 15. horde; 16. heap; 17. drove; 18. mob; 19. school; 20. congregation.

12. CANADIAN BABEL

60 percent: 27 percent of the French speak no English; 13 percent of the English speak no French; therefore 40 percent speak only one language; therefore, 60 percent speak two languages.

13. INTERNATIONAL PERSONNEL KNOWLEDGE

The first one: There is no such thing as a Brazilian language—most Brazilians speak Portuguese.

SCIENCE

1. HOW LAVISH IS NATURE?

1a: The number of stars that can be seen without a telescope from all over the earth is about 7,500.

2c: Molecules would need 100 million years for filling an average light bulb if they entered at the rate of 1 million every second.

3c: Theoretically, the heart is capable of filling a large railroad tank car in three days, or the area of a sky-scraper some 20 stories high in about 70 years.

4b: The eruption of the Krakatau on August 26–27, 1883, was the worst volcanic catastrophe in history. Thirty-six thousand, four hundred and seventeen people were killed, the detonation was heard as far as 3,000 miles away, and windows were shattered within a radius of 500 miles.

5b: At that, dust is particularly light and it takes many billion dust particles to make up a fraction of an ounce.

6c: As devastating and destructive as the effects of atomic bombs are, the area affected is a comparatively small one. A moderate earthquake is considered to be 1,000 times more powerful than the blast of an atomic bomb.

7a: There are many more species but that many have been described by scientists.

8b: Although large meteors are found only occasionally, the earth is hit by these small bodies almost constantly.

9c: This is a number that would yield enough caviar for about 6,000 sandwiches.

10b: This is the average amount found in one cubic millimeter in healthy humans.

11b: The amount of mud and fine sand is three times as high.

12c: Up to 11 milligrams per pound have been found in sea water off California.

2. THE PROBLEM OF THE CHANGING LAB SCENE

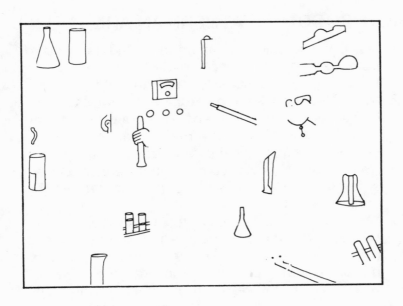

3.   TWO-FACED FREAKS

1e:	Wizard/Lizard	8c:	Layman/Cayman
6i:	Seer/Deer	4g:	Arab/Crab
2a:	Foe/Doe	9d:	Lear/Bear
7h:	Weaver/Beaver	5j:	Cook/Rook
3f:	Coach/Roach	10b:	Monger/Conger

4.   SINK OR SWIM?

1. Swims; 2. Sinks; 3. Sinks; 4. Swims; 5. Swims; 6. Swims; 7. Swims; 8. Swims; 9. Sinks; 10. Sinks; 11. Sinks; 12. Sinks; 13. Swims; 14. Sinks; 15. Swims.

5.   THE PROBLEMATIC HEN PARTY

Number 2 is the heaviest; the rest of the hens, in descending order by weight, are: 3, 4, 5 and 1.

6.   HOW GOOD A WEATHERMAN ARE YOU?

1. *No:* Chinese children can sit for hours listening to quiet stories and are not driven to continuous activity as, for instance, are American children.
2. *No:* While it does happen that early morning rains disappear during the forenoon, more often the day keeps on being rainy. The rhyming of "seven" and "eleven" seems to be the only basis for the "truth."
3. *No:* Statistics show that most babies are conceived at temperatures between 40 and 70 degrees, in the spring and fall.
4. *Yes:* Healthy tissue reacts to humidity of the air. While this in itself cannot be felt, a very specific pain is experienced when such a reaction is interrupted in some places by old scar tissue, all of which is an indicator of changes in humidity which, in turn, indicate a change of weather.

5. *No:* Northerners resist infections better because of their higher body energy level induced by stimulating weather. People coming north succumb more easily to northern diseases like respiratory diseases and tuberculosis.

6. *No:* All this indicates is an upset digestive system on the part of the dog.

7. *Yes:* The old sailing vessels took advantage of this when sailing from Europe to America.

8. *No:* Just the opposite is true. Cumulus clouds are the familiar "wool packs" seen on warm summer days, while nimbus clouds, which are dark irregular masses with very ragged edges and almost shapeless, bring on rain or snow.

9. *Yes:* Some scientists think that the reason may be that our tissues soak up water like a sponge when outer air pressure falls. With rising pressure our spirits rise, too.

10. *No:* The North Pole has long hours of sunlight during this period, but the sun's rays strike at a great slant and do not give as much heat as they do farther south.

11. *Yes:* Many instances are known where lightning has struck repeatedly. The Empire State Building in New York City has an impressive record of being struck by lightning.

12. *Yes:* Caffeine may harmfully excite people already overstimulated by brisk and changing weather while people in the tropics tolerate these stimuli better.

13. *No:* People in temperate zones tolerate alcohol better. Their more active tissues burn it up faster and rid the body of its harmful effect. They may even benefit from the relaxation small quantities bring.

14. *No:* It is far higher at temperatures below 40 degrees Fahrenheit and actually lowest in midsummer.

15. *No:* The usual thickness of the muskrat's fur is due to a good food supply in the year past, and the squirrel gathers all the nuts it can so that a large store points only to a good nut crop.
16. *Yes:* It is made up of a rising current of warm air which may attain a velocity of several hundred miles an hour, and moves from southwest to northeast at from 30 to 60 miles an hour.
17. *No:* Though it has been recorded that storms often follow hectic battles, the explanation lies elsewhere. Troop movements preceding a battle must be carried out in good weather. As these preparations often take several days, the end of a dry spell is usually reached by the time the engagement is fairly begun.
18. *Yes:* Rainbows tell of the presence of showers some distance away. Even if it does not rain at the place of observation, it might well do so a little later.
19. *Yes:* One looks at a watch and notes the seconds that elapse between the flash of lightning and the time when one hears the roll of thunder. At 5 seconds the flash is about one mile away, as sound travels at about 1,090 feet per second.
20. *Yes:* At the same temperature moist air is more productive of heat prostration than dry air, as the cooling system of the body cannot work properly in excessive humidity.
21. *Yes:* During the day warm air over the land is pushed upward by the cool heavy air over the water as it comes in, making a sea breeze. At night, however, the situation is reversed. For the earth not only warms up more quickly than water but also loses its heat more rapidly at night. The land is soon cooler than the water, and the air over it begins to fall and push the warmer air over the water upward, making a land breeze toward the sea.

22. *Yes:* Swallows eat insects of all kinds. During good weather, insects tend to fly fairly high. When the air cools off due to an approaching cold front, insects seek their hideouts below, and the swallows follow them in their search for food.

23. *Yes:* In undisturbed air, at a temperature of 32 degrees, the velocity of sound is approximately 1,090 feet per second. The velocity increases about one foot per second for each degree as the temperature rises.

24. *No:* Statistics show that the general climate of a region averages about the same year after year, and real changes take place only over very long periods of time.

25. *No:* Though it is not known whether they are actually sensitive to atmospheric electricity or to changes in air pressure, their feeling is not imaginary. The same behavior can be observed in certain wild and domestic animals, especially dogs. Cats do not seem to be much affected, but other animals, some with a very low scale of evolution, show similar behavior. Since the actual events of a thunderstorm should not influence their habits of life, the guess at sensitivity of some kind to atmospheric electricity seems justified.

7. ANIMAL DOUBLE-TALK

Dog Words: 1. Boxer; 2. Pointer; 3. Chow; 4. Pekingese; 5. Husky; 6. Pug; 7. Setter; 8. Newfoundland.
Horse Words: 1. Pony; 2. Bay; 3. Mount; 4. Arab; 5. Colt; 6. Jade; 7. Clipper; 8. Mare.
Bird Words: 1. Adjutant; 2. Cardinal; 3. Rook; 4. Bunting; 5. Lark; 6. Turkey; 7. Crane; 8. Stilt.
Fish Words: 1. Bass; 2. Fluke; 3. Perch; 4. Pike; 5. Skate; 6. Ruff; 7. Ray; 8. Sole.

8. DO YOU KNOW THE TIMES OF THEIR LIVES?

1. *Whale,* 75 years; Elephant, 65 years.
2. *Horse,* 22 years; Antelope, 12 years.
3. *Gorilla,* 28 years; Dog, 18 years.
4. *Leopard,* 28 years; Moose, 18 years.
5. *Hippopotamus,* 35 years; Giraffe, 25 years.
6. *Camel,* 22 years; Coyote, 12 years.
7. *Porpoise,* 32 years; Buffalo, 22 years.
8. *Lion,* 20 years; Fox, 10 years.
9. *Bear,* 28 years; Cat, 18 years.
10. *Tiger,* 25 years; Cow, 15 years.

9. FALLACIOUS, ISN'T IT?

4, 7, 9, 2, 10, 1, 3, 6, 5 and 8.

10. DON'T LET THESE TREES STUMP YOU!

Winner was number *5:* Next were 3, 1, 2, 6 and 4.

11. SOUND TRACK AT THE ZOO

1. Mew, meow, purr, yowl and caterwaul; 2. Grunt; 3. Bellow, roar; 4. Quack; 5. Hiss, blow; 6. Cackle, cluck, chuck; 7. Trumpet; 8. Squeak, cheep; 9. Roar; 10. Gaggle; 11. Moo, low; 12. Howl; 13. Bray; 14. Croak; 15. Buzz, hum, drone; 16. Chatter; 17. Squeal; 18. Bell; 19. Bleat; 20. Caw, croak; 21. Gaggle, hiss, cackle, gabble; 22. Bleat; 23. Drone, boom; 24. Hoot, screech.

12. COLORFUL NONSENSE

Blue: Every pair of items has the colors reversed here.

13. CONSERVATION, PLEASE!

By letting the steer live.

14. DAMN THE MOSQUITOES!

Why not? Enough of them might weigh a pound, and the logs they sit on have bark.

15. KNOW YOUR ENEMY

1. *True:* And only the female mosquito can stab you. The mouth of the male is not equipped to suck blood; he lives on plant juices. Of all insects, the sting of the hornet is the worst, followed by the stings of the yellow jacket, wasp, and honeybee.
2. *True:* But they are relatives of insects. Insects are segmented and have three pairs of legs. Whereas a spider, for example, has four pairs of legs. Some 700,000 different species of insects have been classified, more than twice the number of species of plants and all other animals put together.
3. *False:* According to the Pasteur Institute, a fly may live as long as 62 days, sometimes longer. Bees live about six weeks, and queen termites 50 years.
4. *False:* Bees do die after they sting, not immediately but after one or two days. A sting is harmless unless a person is allergic to it, and unless it is near the eyes or the mouth.
5. *False:* Some female mosquitoes that "stab" don't hum, or their hum is too high for us to hear. The male mosquito, which doesn't attack, also hums.
6. *False:* Mosquitoes in your home, for instance, may take refuge on dark rather than light things—black clothing rather than blue or brown. Forgetting about insecticides, which may make life as miserable for you as for mosquitoes, there is no foolproof way to guarantee a night of freedom. But try ridding your room of the pests with a vacuum cleaner; you'll soon find their favorite haunts. If you are stung and have no lotion handy, lathering the affected area with ordinary soap should relieve the itch.

7. *False:* The fireflies we see usually begin flashing at dusk and usually stop when it is fully dark.

8. *False:* Like lobsters, insects have skeletons outside their bodies (called exoskeletons); they have brains as complex as the brains of vertebrates; and, though entirely different from man's, they have hearts, blood, glands (salivary, hair, wax, etc.), and all the senses that man has—hearing, touch, taste, smell and sight.

9. *False:* Insects are the toughest of all creatures. They can survive the coldest winters simply by freezing solid and remaining in a state of suspended animation until spring comes to thaw them out. But spells of warm weather followed by re-freezing may kill them.

10. *False:* There are more different insects in the tropics, but in numbers, scientists say, the temperate zones may be first.

11. *False:* Houseflies are responsible for transmitting cases of tuberculosis, typhoid, cholera, yaws and so on. Moral: Don't leave food uncovered during the summer.

12. *False:* Insects are found nearly everywhere—from the Arctic to the equator to the Antarctic. They're cold-blooded and can adapt to any environment where there is food in the form of plants and animals.

13. *False:* Most insects do get tired, and their condition while resting can properly be called sleep.

14. *True:* But they will be comparatively inert; they won't, for example, go looking for food.

15. *False:* Only a few hundred of the 700,000 known insect species are decidedly harmful to man. Most insects fulfill important roles, such as pollination of many essential plants; production of useful items like honey, silk and dyes; control of noxious weeds and harmful insects; loosening soil; and serving as food for many animals, and primitive men, too.

FINE ARTS

1. ## WHOSE PRICELESS THOUGHTS?

   Art expert: 1. Annabelle; 2. Frederick; 3. Patrick; 4. Kate; 5. Felix; 6. Philippa; 7. Humphrey; 8. Ebenezer; 9. Ethelbert.

2. ## CAN YOU SET THE QUARTET?

   Arthur, piano; Bert, cello; Clare, violin; David, flute: Arthur cannot be the cellist because the cellist has a long ride home. The cellist, therefore, must be Bert, the bachelor. Arthur must be the pianist, as a piano cannot be put on a Christmas table. David, who got a book from the violinist, cannot himself be the violinist and must, therefore, be the flutist, while Clare must be the violinist.

3. ## DOUBLE ARTISTRY IN A SPLIT SECOND?

   He does not fit, alas.

4. ## OH, SWEET MYSTERY OF MODERN ART!

   1e, 2c, 3i, 4b, 5h, 6j, 7a, 8g, 9f, 10d.

5. ## ADDLED ARTISTS IN THE GOOFY GALLERY

   1. The saw belongs to a later period. 2. A whale in a lake. 3. Elephant without tusks. 4. One cord of swing not connected. 5. Television antenna in medieval scene. 6. Glasses on knight. 7. Tail is not one of a horse. 8. Automobile between engine and railroad car. 9. Boy in shopping net. 10. Black keys in front of piano. 11. Electric plug in medieval scene. 12. Church and tree cast different shadows. 13. Newspaper logo upside down.

6. HOW POP "ART"FUL ARE YOU?

The dotted pattern with 19 small squares: The whole diagram can be partitioned into 7 by 12 small squares. The others follow in descending order:

Bricklike: 15 squares
Black: 14 squares
White: 13 squares
Diagonal: 12 squares
Linear: 11 squares

7. MORE POP "ART"FULNESS

None: If you look closely, there are only straight lines.

8. SCOTTIES, SCOTTIES EVERYWHERE

One black, two white, and ten black and white.

SOCIAL STUDIES

GEOGRAPHY

1. METROPOLITAN LANDMARKS

1. Paris (Eiffel Tower); 2. Cairo (Pyramids); 3. London (Big Ben); 4. Washington (Capitol Building); 5. New York (Empire State Building); 6. Rome (Colosseum); 7. Moscow (Kremlin); 8. Tokyo (Mount Fujiyama); 9. Athens (Acropolis); 10. Berlin (Brandenburg Gate).

2.   WATCH YOUR STEP!

You are on the exact spot where the equator and the international dateline meet: in the central Pacific near the Gilbert Islands.

3.   WATCH THAT STATE LINE!

We never heard of a peacock laying an egg.

4.   COUNTRIES, ISLANDS, AND TOWNS— WITHOUT CAPITALS, THEY'RE NOUNS!

1. Turkey; 2. Panama; 3. Morocco; 4. Brazil; 5. Canaries; 6. Holland; 7. Chile; 8. China; 9. Guinea; 10. Curaçao; 11. Japan; 12. Cyprus; 13. Phoenix; 14. Boston; 15. Bologna; 16. Cayenne; 17. Madras; 18. Flint; 19. Delft; 20. Leghorn; 21. Tuxedo; 22. Orange; 23. Hull; 24. Limerick.

5.   ARE YOU AN INTERNATIONAL CLOTHES-SLEUTH?

1g: American; 2i: Japanese; 3k: Tibetan; 4h: Indian; 5j: Hollander; 6d: Hungarian; 7a: Spaniard; 8e: Greek; 9b: Bedouin; 10f: Scotchman; 11c: Russian.

6.   TALL TALES FROM THE SOUTH

Three: There can only be a north wind at the South Pole. You can leave the South Pole only in a northern direction. There are not a few hours, but six months, between sunset and sunrise with only one sunset in the fall, and one sunrise in the spring.

7.   . . . AND A PUZZLING SNAPSHOT FROM MEXICO

The first and the next to the last.

8. WHERE TO FIND A REPRESENTATIVE ABROAD

1o, 2l, 3k, 4f, 5t, 6n, 7a, 8s, 9p, 10q, 11i, 12e, 13d, 14m, 15r, 16g, 17j, 18h, 19b and 20c.

HISTORY

1. WHO SAID WHAT IN AMERICA?

1c, 2i, 3n, 4h, 5d, 6m, 7k, 8j, 9f, 10a, 11g, 12e, 13b, 14o and 15l.

2. PRESIDENTIAL WORD FORMULA

Pierce: recipe.

3. HOW "SHIPSHAPE" ARE YOU?

1. *Hannah;* 2. *Santa Maria;* 3. *Mayflower;* 4. *Bounty;* 5. *Missouri;* 6. *Bellerophon;* 7. *Titanic;* 8. *Maine;* 9. *Lusitania;* 10. *Graf Spee;* 11. *Merrimac;* 12. *Monitor.*

4. CONSTITUTIONAL CHESTNUTS

Because sometimes the ayes have it, and sometimes the noes. Pro and con.

5. THE MIXED-UP MIDDLE AGES

1. Cigarette; 2. cigarette lighter; 3. stroller; 4. balloon; 5. watch; 6. potato (unknown then); 7. bananas (unknown then); 8. dollar sign; 9. umbrella; 10. American flag; 11. "Cinema"; 12. pocketbook; 13. traffic signal; 14. light bulb; 15. "Nelson" Street; 16. hobbyhorse; 17. spectacles; 18. jet plane; 19. television antenna.

6.   WHO WAS "I"?

1e, 2d, 3f, 4g, 5b, 6a, 7l, 8k, 9j, 10h, 11i and 12c.

7.   PIECEMEAL PEACE MEAL

8.   WHO'S IN WHOM?

1e: Elias HOWE; 2s: Johann Sebastian BACH; 3n: John MILTON; 4j: any of the czars IVAN; 5k: Gregor Johann MENDEL; 6o: Mark HOPKINS; 7r: Alessandro VOLTA; 8p: William Jennings BRYAN; 9t: Oscar STRAUS; 10f: Vivien LEIGH; 11h: Thomas MANN; 12g: Bob HOPE; 13d: Frans HALS; 14a: ADAM; 15b: ABEL; 16l: Crawford Williamson LONG; 17i: Anthony EDEN; 18m: ISRAEL; 19c: Alexander Graham BELL; 20q: Jenny LIND.

9. WORDS IN INDEPENDENCE DAY

1. Epee; 2. Pence; 3. Deep; 4. Deepen; 5. Depend; 6. Need; 7. Decay; 8. Indeed; 9. Dace; 10. Dance; 11. Peace; 12. Cane; 13. Deny; 14. Dependency: 15. Decade; 16. Dane; 17. Dead; 18. Dean; 19. Pend; 20. Peen.

HOME ECONOMICS

1. ADD THE "INGREDIENTS" AND EAT YOUR MENU!

1. Sardine; 2. Olives; 3. Onions; 4. Borscht; 5. Beans; 6. Venison; 7. Gravy; 8. Pastry; 9. Rarebits; 10. Candies; 11. Dates.

2. CAN YOU SPOT THE TWIN COOKS?

Numbers 11 and 16.

3. POT AND PITCHER LOGIC

Item number 5: The item must be a teapot, and its handle must be turned outward as in row 1, but the black-and-white pattern must be the reverse of the pattern in row 1.

4. TO EACH HIS OWN—CAKE!

1. Date Cake; 2. Ribbon Cake; 3. Layer Cake; 4. Marble Cake; 5. Spice Cake; 6. Cheesecake; 7. Sunshine Cake; 8. Imperial Cake; 9. Shortcake; 10. Loaf Cake; 11. Wedding Cake; 12. Round Cake.

5. ARE YOU A KITCHEN DETECTIVE?

Because the dumplings in the heated soup were still cold, which they wouldn't be if the soup had been cooked fresh.

6. "EGG"OCENTRIC HOUSEWIFE

Six.

7. HOUSEHOLD TRUTHS OR MYTHS?

1. *False:* The moths lay eggs in suitable material; these eggs develop into larvae which then eat the clothes.
2. *False:* It is impossible to see dust by ordinary light; when the dust particles are highly illuminated, they become visible, but not more numerous.
3. *False:* Carbon monoxide is tasteless and has only a faint smell, but it is a deadly poison.
4. *True:* Experiments have proven that they can be hard boiled later.
5. *False:* It is highly nutritious; however, when sold as whole milk it constitutes a fraud, as milk is more expensive than skim milk.
6. *False:* The fact is that the best method to purify water is simply to let it stand.
7. *False:* When the wine is hermetically sealed in a glass bottle, it can neither lose nor gain alcoholic strength.
8. *False:* The color of an eggshell has nothing to do with its richness.
9. *False:* What happens is that by taking in more heat and then cooling down to the same temperature one had before one may *seem* to be cooler.
10. *True:* This is due to fundamental physical laws.

11. *False:* Sunshine is more desirable in drying clothes than a high wind since sunshine both sweetens and blanches them, while a high wind may tear the clothes and may take the stiffness out of starched goods.

12. *False:* It is the freezing process that causes pipes to burst; the bursting is due to the expansion the water undergoes when changing into ice.

8. ON HEAD OR FOOT?

1. H; 2. H; 3. F; 4. F; 5. H; 6. H; 7. F; 8. H; 9. F; 10. H; 11. H; 12. F; 13. F; 14. H; 15. H; 16. F; 17. F; 18. H; 19. H; 20. F.

9. PICK YOUR PATTERN!

Number 7.

10. PICK UP THE PIECES!

Six dishes, as in illustration below:

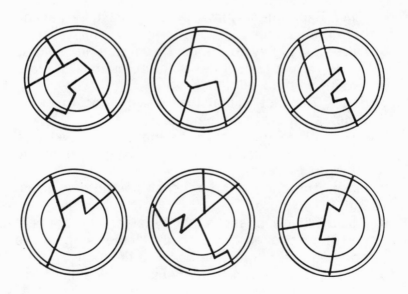

11. EAT YOUR WORD TOTALS!

1. Pump/kin; 2. Ban/ana; 3. En/dive; 4. Muff/in; 5. Man/go; 6. Pa/paw; 7. Cur/rant; 8. Had/dock; 9. Chic/ken; 10. Can/ape; 11. Pep/per; 12. So/up; 13. Cut/let.

12. BOTTLE IMPERFECTION

Number 1 and number 5 in the third row.

ABOUT THE AUTHOR:

Gerard Mosler is one of the leading experts in the puzzle field, with countless contributions to almost all leading magazines and a number of books to his credit— among them the American Heritage and Horizon Crossword Puzzle Books, the Parent's Magazine Press Family Quiz Book, *Sharpen Your Wits* published by Doubleday, and several Scholastic puzzle books for youngsters. Mr. and Mrs. Mosler live in Forest Hills, N.Y.

ABOUT THE ARTIST:

Frank C. Smith has only recently added his talents to illustrating children's books, having worked in advertising and public relations and as an actor in television. He presently lives with his wife in Reseda, California, where he works as a cartoonist for the Walt Disney Studios.